MW00388160

A special thanks
to everyone
who has helped make
Know Yourself
what it is today.

Dear Reader

Knowing yourself is truly the beginning of all wisdom. We give young learners the building blocks they need to start their unique journey of self-discovery: an understanding of human anatomy — literally how we are put together. Knowledge of one's own human body is an empowering context on which anyone can build.

Learning about the body and mind at a young age sets the foundation for honoring one's physical form, develops self-esteem and self-confidence, and begins the discovery of who we are meant to be in this world.

Now that's real power.

The Know Yourself Team

Quick-Start Guide

Hello Know Yourselfers!

Follow these steps to start a new journey and explore the skeletal system. Have fun and remember - knowledge is the skeleton for new ideas!

1

Grab your winter clothing and pelmeni! We are going to Russia.

Locate Russia on your atlas, or find an online map of the world.

2

Read Time Skaters Adventure 2.

Pinky and Bounski continue the search, meeting Alexander Maximov at the Karl May School, but they'll need each other if they're going to get out.

3

Get equipped!

Gather your supplies and prepare for your activities. These supplies are your precursors to some fun learning.

Table of Contents

Hello Adventurer!

Welcome to Adventure 2 - The Skeletal System.

In this workbook, you will learn about Russia in the early and mid-20th Century and your body's Skeletal System There will be information to read, activities to complete, and quizzes to take when you are ready to challenge yourself! Take your time along the way - spend as much or as little time as you like on each activity, and do not forget to use additional resources to learn more about the topics you are interested in.

Good luck, and have fun!

Can you find St. Petersburg, Russia?

THE TIME TRAVEL CLOCK READS
1922

Get ready for a bone-chilling adventure!

Добро пожаловать!

(Dobro Pozhalovat)*
That means "Welcome!" in Russian.

***Say it like this:** "doh-**bro** – pas-**zha**-low-vat."
*Syllables in bold are the strongest.

**This portal
will lead you to...**

Time Skaters Adventure 2

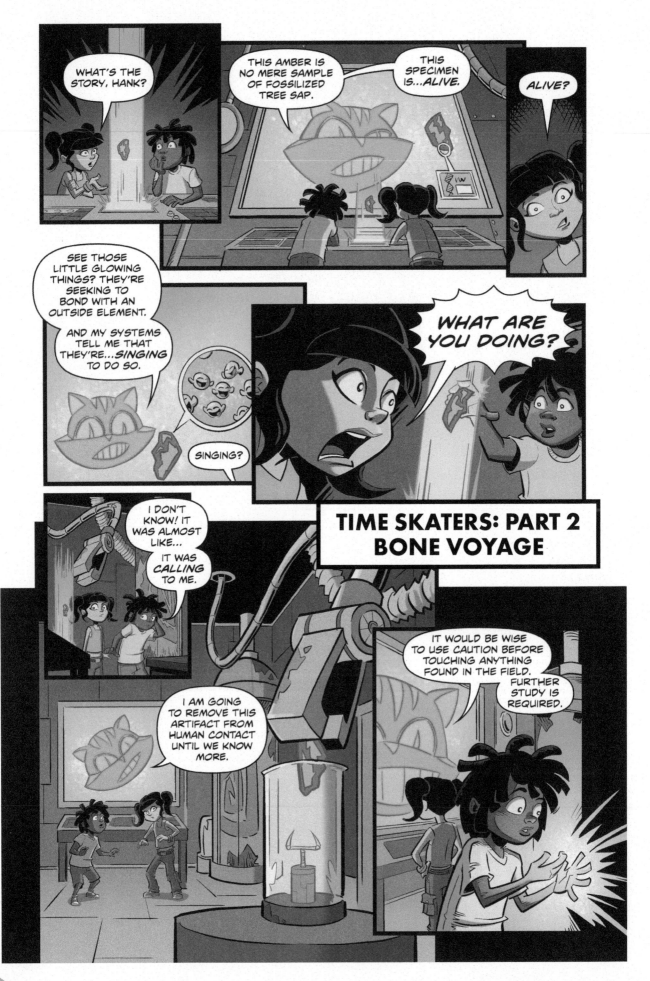

TIME SKATERS: PART 2
BONE VOYAGE

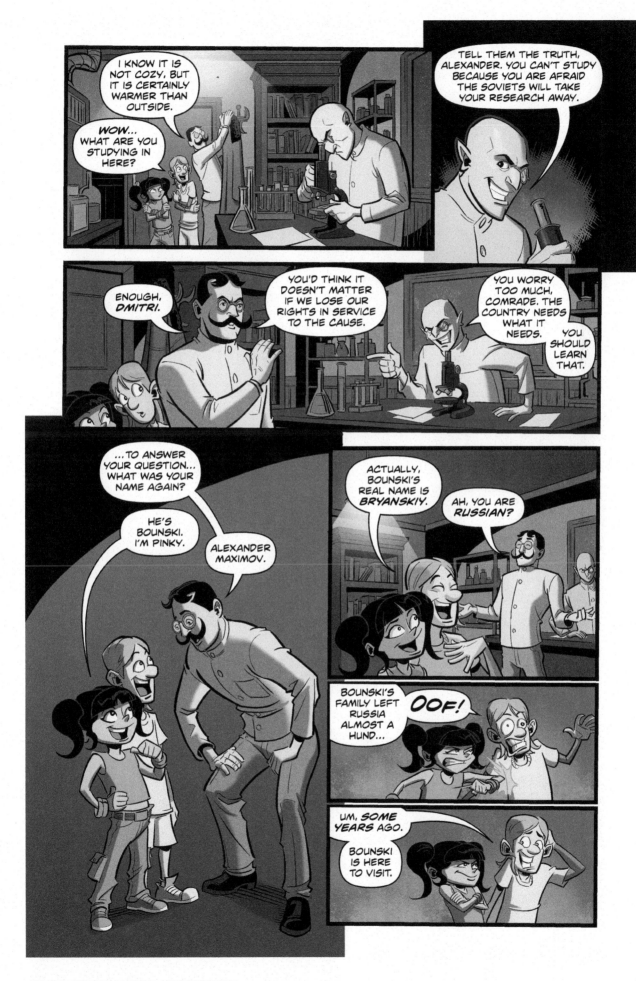

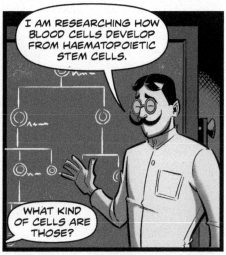

Learning Calendar

Part 1

Know Your History

Estimated hours
5 hours
of fun

Gather the adventure equipment you'll need from around the house - find the checklist on pages 22 and 23!

Locate Russia on a world map using a globe, an atlas, or an online map (like this one: https://knowyourself.com/maps)

Read the comic **Time Skaters: Part 2 - Bone Voyage**. Find it at the beginning of this Adventure Guide!

Read about Russia in *Know Your History*.

Study the masters in *Know Your Art*.

Binge on books with *Know Your Novelists*.

Fabricating *like Fabergé*.

Soar among the stars in *Space Racing*.

Write *like a Russian*.

Complete *20th Century Russia Crossword*.

Test all *Tsar Knowledge!*

Part 2

Know Your Skeletal System

Study the skeleton in *Know Your Skeletal System*.

Pull yourself together in *A Bone to Pick*.

Dance your way through *A Bony Twist!*

Think *on your feet!*
Get that *Posture en Pointe.*

Detangle the *Skeletal System Word Search.*

Answer a *Skele-ton of Information.*

Part **3**

Know Your Appetite

Read *Know Your Appetite.*

Read the recipes on the following pages. Make a shopping list, purchase ingredients, and get your kitchen ready!

Make *Russian Potato Salad with Dill* and *Sushkis.*

Share your dishes with your family. Discuss *Thoughts for Young Chefs* around the table!

Part **4**

Show What You Know!

Rush In *and Bone Up.*

Check out *Further Reading* for more opportunities to learn.

Great job Adventurer!

Home Inventory Checklist

Ask your parents to help you find these items around the house. These are some of the tools you will need on your adventure.

- [ ] **Colored pencils**
  - Know Your Art, A Bone to Pick, Think on Your Feet! Posture en Pointe

- [ ] **A container -- this can be a cardboard box, an empty pringles can, a plastic egg or anything else you can think of!**
  - Fabricating like Fabergé

- [ ] **Glue stick or school glue**
  - Fabricating like Fabergé

- [ ] **Colored markers**
  - Fabricating like Fabergé, A Bony Twist!

- [ ] **Blank paper**
  - Fabricating like Fabergé

- [ ] **Other decorative materials -- think Plastic jewels, glitter, beads, etc.**
  - Fabricating like Fabergé

- [ ] **Newspaper**
  - Space Racing

- [ ] **A round balloon**
  - Space Racing

- [ ] **A wide cup or bowl**
  - Space Racing

- [ ] **White glue**
  - Space Racing

- [ ] **Water**
  - Space Racing

✓ *Check the items off when you've found them!*

☐ **A spoon**
- Space Racing

☐ **Paintbrushes**
- Space Racing

☐ **Acrylic paints (white or yellow, gray)**
- Space Racing

☐ **Scissors**
- Space Racing, A Bone To Pick

☐ **Blank paper**
- Writing Like A Russian, A Bone To Pick, A Bony Twist!

☐ **Printed Skeleton Pages**
- A Bone To Pick

☐ **Tape**
- A Bone To Pick

☐ **Hole puncher**
- A Bone To Pick

☐ **Your completed skeleton from *"A Bone to Pick"***
- A Bony Twist!, Know Yourself, Draw Yourself!

☐ **Music**
- A Bony Twist!

☐ **Paper you don't care about. It can be junk mail!**
- Mighty Bones

☐ **Colored chalk**
- Know Yourself, Draw Yourself!

☐ **A dry sidewalk**
- Know Yourself, Draw Yourself!

Be creative *if you don't have something on the list.*

Know Your History

Russia, 1922

Alexander Maximov was a Russian histologist a scientist who studies the anatomy of cells and tissues. He was born and raised in the city of St. Petersburg
and later received his degree as a medical doctor where he worked as a professor. Maximov created the term "stem cell" and demonstrated that all blood cells develop from a common earlier type of cell, called a precursor.
He fled St. Petersburg in 1922, traveling to the United States to teach anatomy at the University of Chicago.

St. Petersburg is the second-largest city in Russia and the most northern major city in the world. It is located on the Baltic Sea, and is a busy port. St. Petersburg is also an important cultural area. Numerous monuments are located there, such as The Mariinsky Opera and Ballet Theater, The Imperial Palace, and The Hermitage, one of the largest art museums in the world.

St. Petersburg

Vladimir Lenin was one of the most influential rulers in Russian history. He lived during a time when the tsar,* or ruler, had absolute power in Russia. Peasants and workers had nothing. In October 1917, Lenin and his supporters, the Bolsheviks, overthrew the government and began the fight to turn Russia into a communist country. Under communism, the government owns everything, including land and factories.

tsar

*Say it like this: "zar".

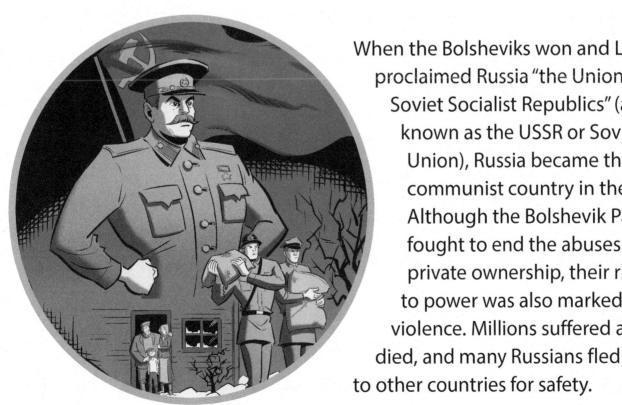

When the Bolsheviks won and Lenin proclaimed Russia "the Union of Soviet Socialist Republics" (also known as the USSR or Soviet Union), Russia became the first communist country in the world. Although the Bolshevik Party fought to end the abuses of private ownership, their rise to power was also marked by violence. Millions suffered and died, and many Russians fled to other countries for safety.

Look at all of these dolls! They are called Russian nesting dolls, or **matryoshka***, if you happen to speak Russian.

matryoshka

***Say it like this:** "ma-tree-**osh**-ka".*

Syllables in bold are the strongest.

If you look closely, you'll notice something interesting about these hand-painted wooden dolls:

they fit inside of each other!

Inside of each doll is a smaller version of the same doll, and inside of that one is an even smaller one. This onion-like characteristic has led people to think that the dolls represent the many layers of Russian personality.

Now grab some crayons or colored pencils.

Color them in!

Know Your Art

Get creative with colors.

Know Your Art

Now draw your own **matryoshka**.

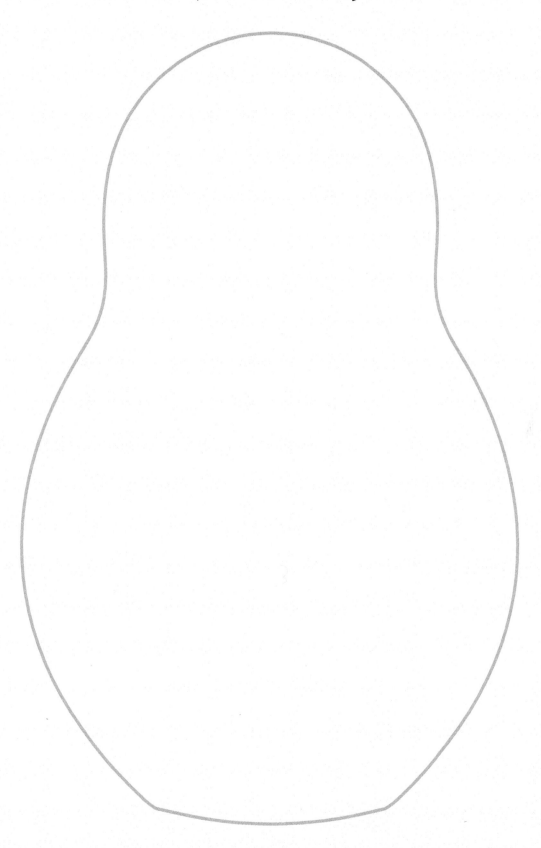

Know Your Novelists

In addition to hearty foods and beautiful ballet, Russian culture has produced many famous authors over the centuries. Some well-known Russian writers include **Leo Tolstoy** (author of War and Peace), **Fyodor Dostoyevsky** (author of Crime and Punishment), and **Boris Pasternak** (author of Doctor Zhivago).

As well as being wonderful storytellers, these Russian authors tried to answer philosophical questions about truth, knowledge, and the world.

Try thinking about these:

- Does your definition of "**doing the right thing**" change day to day or is it always the same?

- Do people have to be **sad sometimes** to be **happy at other times**?

- Which is more important, **imagination** or **knowledge**?

These examples of philosophical questions can't be answered only by scientific knowledge or only by our own experience. They demand lots of thinking, and often lead to more and more questions.

Can you think of a philosophical question of your own?

_____

_____

_____

_____

_____

_____

 Share on social media:

#KnowYourAdventure

 KnowYourselfOAK   **KnowYourselfOAK**

Fabricating like Fabergé

Russia is a land known for many beautiful buildings and wonderful works of art. Among the most famous treasures that were created under the Tsars are the **Fabergé eggs**. First commissioned in 1885 as an Easter gift, these increasingly extravagant tiny works of art were crafted each year by **Peter Carl Fabergé** and a team of craftsmen, who were only instructed that each one needed a surprise and to be entirely unique!

Materials:

- **A container** - this can be a cardboard box, an empty pringles can, a plastic egg or anything else you can think of!

- **Glue stick or school glue**

- **Colored markers**

- **Blank paper**

- **Other decorative materials** - think plastic jewels, glitter, beads, etc.

Directions:

1. Determine what you want to use your container for. Is it going to hide a surprise, like the Tsar's eggs did, or will you use it for your valuables?

2. Decide on a design. The eggs Peter Fabergé made were sketched out before they were finally put together. Using a blank piece of paper, you can sketch out what you want to put onto your box.

3. Use your markers, colored paper, glitter, and other supplies to bring your container to life!

   Often, Fabergé eggs use lines around the entire egg to create a pleasing pattern. Use paper or plastic jewels to accentuate points and provide depth. Just make sure you don't prevent your container from opening!

Space Racing

Have you ever stargazed into the night sky, thinking about
"What it would be like to travel in space?"
If so, you're not alone!

Space exploration became a major interest to the United States and the Soviet Union during the Cold War. World War II began in 1939 and was known as the largest and most violent war in history.

During World War II, German Nazi leader Adolf Hitler signed a pact with Soviet Union leader Joseph Stalin called the German-Soviet Nonaggression Pact. The order agreed that the two parties would be peaceful and not take any military action towards each other for 10 years. Adolf Hitler broke the pact by sending troops to invade the Soviet Union, effectively entering Germany into war with the Soviet Union.

The battle of Stalingrad, won by the Soviet Union, helped to end World War II. During World War II, there was peace between the United States and the Soviet Union as they both sought to defeat Hitler during the end of World War II.

After World War II, the Soviet Union and the United States became known as the strongest powers in the world. This rivalry for power became known as the Cold War. While no direct battle occurred during the Cold War, the Soviet Union and the United States competed to obtain superior military standing during this time.

One belief during the Cold War was that the United States and the Soviet Union saw space travel as a symbol of power and advanced scientific achievement.

1957 | The Soviet Union launched the first artificial satellite, named "**Sputnik**", to orbit the earth.

1958 | The United States launched its first satellite, "**Explorer 1**," and so began the "**Space Race**"!

1961 | Soon after, the Soviets sent the first man to space.

1969 | The United States achieved putting the first man on the moon.

Space Racing

**Adventurers, can you imagine
sending your own satellite into outer space
or landing on the moon?**

Let's try making your own moon using the materials below.

Materials:

- **Newspaper**
- **A round balloon**
- **A wide cup or bowl**
- **White glue**

- **Water**
- **A spoon**
- **Paintbrushes**
- **Acrylic paints** (white or yellow, gray)
- **Scissors**

Directions:

1. First, lay out a few sheets of newspaper to protect your workstation.

2. Next, blow up a round balloon and set it aside. Later you will use this balloon as the base for your moon.

3. Next tear long, thick strips of newspaper with your hands (about 1 inch in thickness is the goal but do not worry if each one comes out a little bit different).

4. Now, prepare your moon glue in a cup or bowl by mixing equal parts water and glue. Stir with spoon.

5. Form the first moon layer by taking strips of torn newspaper from your pile and dipping them in the moon glue, squeezing out any excess glue by sliding your fingers down either side of the newspaper. Then wrap each piece around the balloon, smoothing out any bumps as you go with your fingers. Complete the first layer by covering every spot you can see on the balloon. Just leave an open section around the balloon knot - you will need this opening to remove the balloon once your project is dry.

6. Create 2 more layers of paper all over the balloon.

7. Allow your project to completely dry overnight, untouched until tomorrow.

8. Once your project is completely dry, you can paint your moon using white or yellow paint for the base and the gray paint for any craters you can imagine you are on the moon. Have fun!

9. When the moon paint is dry, make a small hole near the knot of the balloon using your scissors. While the balloon is deflating, hold onto the knot with your other hand. Once fully deflated, you can remove it through the opening.

For more fun, take your moon and head outside in the evening to gaze up at the stars.

What do you see?

Ask an adult to find where you should stargaze.

Writing Like a Russian

The Russian language shares many letters with English, but it also contains many of its own letters! Instead of the 26 letters you may be familiar with in English, there are 33 letters in the **Cyrillic alphabet** that Russian uses.

Some letters may also look familiar, but sound entirely different than you would expect from reading English. For example, A sounds like the English A, and Б sounds like the English B, but the Cyrillic В actually stands for a sound more like the English V!

To help English readers pronounce names and other words, linguists use a process called "**transliteration**", which comes up with an equivalent letter or series of letters to match.

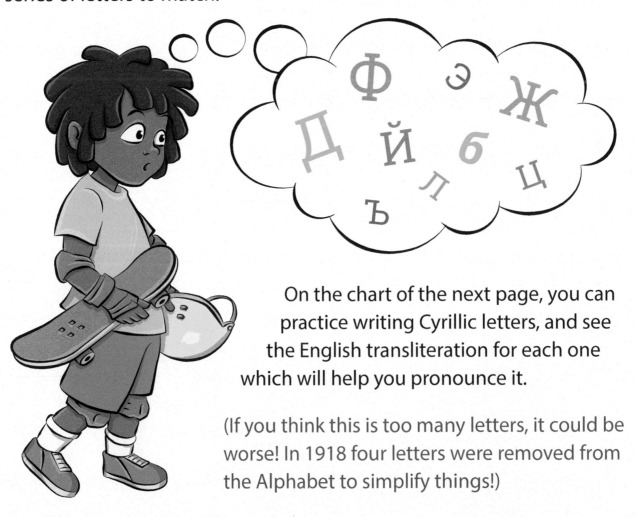

On the chart of the next page, you can practice writing Cyrillic letters, and see the English transliteration for each one which will help you pronounce it.

(If you think this is too many letters, it could be worse! In 1918 four letters were removed from the Alphabet to simplify things!)

А -a	Л -l	Ч -ch
Б -b	М -m	Ш -sh
В -v	Н -n	Щ -shch
Г -g	О -o	Ъ -"(*)
Д -d	П -p	Ы -y
Е -e	Р -r	Ь -'(*)
Ё -yo	С -s	Э -e
Ж -zh	Т -t	Ю -yu
З -z	У -u	Я -ya
И -i	Ф -f	
Й -y	Х -kh	
К -k	Ц -ts	

* These two letters are actually silent! They both change how the letter that comes before them is pronounced.

Writing Like a Russian

The **Cyrillic alphabet** is used in more than fifty languages - Russian, Serbian, Bulgarian, and Macedonian are just a few! It may look strange, but see how you feel after tracing a few letters using the practice sheets.

Ц

Ч

Ш

Щ

Ъ

Ы

Ь

Э

Ю

Я

Expand Your Russian

Now that you know how to pronounce Russian letters, see if you can figure out how to pronounce some common Russian phrases! We've included a few here for you to test out.

Доброе утро	Good Morning
Здравствуйте	Hello
Рад тебя видеть	Nice to see you
Простите	Sorry!
Спасибо	Thank you
Как Вас зовут?	What's your name?
Меня зовут	My Name Is
Пока!	Bye!

Как Вас зовут?

Меня зовут Pinky!

In case you forgot the sound of some letters, here is the **English transliteration** to help you pronounce them.

А -a	И -i	С -s	Ъ -"(*)
Б -b	Й -y	Т -t	Ы -y
В -v	К -k	У -u	Ь -'(*)
Г -g	Л -l	Ф -f	Э -e
Д -d	М -m	Х -kh	Ю -yu
Е -e	Н -n	Ц -ts	Я -ya
Ё -yo	О -o	Ч -ch	
Ж -zh	П -p	Ш -sh	*Silent letters change how the letter that comes before is pronounced.
З -z	Р -r	Щ -shch	

20th Century Russia Crossword

After you finish,
check the answer key on page 110.

Across:

4. Another name for Vladimir Lenin's supporters.

6. A famous ballet dancer may be seen at the _____ Opera and Ballet Theater.

7. The second largest city in Russia and most northern major city in the world.

9. The last name of the Russian histologist who created the term 'stem cell'.

10. Space exploration was a major interest to the United States and Soviet Union during the _____ War.

Down:

1. A cheerful ring-shaped breadstick, popular in Russia.

2. This influential figure led the overthrow of the government, proclaiming Russia as 'The Union of Soviet Socialist Republics'.

3. Someone who ruled with absolute power in Russia, before 1917.

5. 'The Union of Soviet Socialist Republics' also went by '_____ Union'.

8. St. Petersburg, a port city, is located in the _____ Sea.

All Tsar Knowledge

Good work, adventurers!
Now that you have read some things about the history of early 20th century Russia, let's review what you have learned!

Try to fill in the blanks.

During the early 20th century, Alexander Maximov, a __ __ __ __ __ __ __ __ __ __ __ __ __

created the term "stem cell" and demonstrated that all blood cells develop from

a __ __ __ __ __ __ __ __ __ __. Alexander fled St. Petersburg in __ __ __ __ ,

traveling to the United States to teach __ __ __ __ __ __ __ __ .

St. Petersburg is the most __ __ __ __ __ __ __ __ __ major city in the world.

Its many monuments contribute to the cultural importance that St. Petersburg

has to Russia. Monuments you may find visiting are The Mariinsky Opera

& Ballet Theater, The Imperial __ __ __ __ __ __ , and The Hermitage.

In the time before __ __ __ __ __ __ __ __ __ __ __ __ __ and the Bolsheviks had

overthrown the government and fought for Russia to be a __ __ __ __ __ __ __ __ __ __ __

country, the tsar ruled over the country with __ __ __ __ __ __ __ __ __ power.

The struggle to end private ownership and the Bolshevik party's rise to __ __ __ __ __ was marked by violence. One famous treasure, created under tsar rule were the extravagant __ __ __ __ __ __ __ __ eggs, first made as an __ __ __ __ __ __ __ gift.

After the death of Vladimir Lenin, Joseph __ __ __ __ __ __ __ led the Soviet __ __ __ __ __ __ __ through both World War II and the Cold War. While World War II was known for being the most deadly war in history, no direct war ever took place during the __ __ __ __ __ __ __ __. The Cold War was a result of tension between the __ __ __ __ __ __ __ __ __ __ __ __ __ __ and the Soviet Union and their desires to be the strongest __ __ __ __ __ __ __ __ __ __ power in the world. __ __ __ __ __ __ __ __ exploration was symbolic of power and __ __ __ __ __ __ __ __ __ __ __ __ __ __ achievement at that time.

Bonus: How many letters does the Russian language use?

__ __ __

Very nice work, Adventurer!

You can check your answers using the key on page 108.

The Skeleton Scene!

Bone up on BONES!

You've probably been out trick-or-treating on Halloween night, so you might think you know all about skeletons. But do you know that the skeletal system isn't just bones? In addition to the 206 bones that make up the adult skeleton, the skeletal system also includes ligaments, tendons, and cartilage. These are necessary for your bones to move.

Your body gets a structure and form from your bones. Bones also do other things. Take a look!

Some bones, like those in your arms, legs, and spine, help you move around – another word for this is **locomotion**.

Other bones, like those in your skull, rib cage and spine, surround and protect fragile tissue within. For example, your back bones, also known as vertebrae, shield your spinal cord from injuries that could damage it and affect your ability to move. Your skull protects your brain, and your rib cage protects your internal organs such as your heart and lungs.

You're born with about 300 bones. Some bones fuse together as you get older, leaving a new bone total of about 206.

Did you know that your skeleton is made up of two parts?

Your **Axial Skeleton*** includes the bones of your head, face, neck, spine, and rib cage. It provides a framework to give your body shape. Movements of the axial skeleton are not as flexible as those of the appendicular skeleton.

Your **Appendicular Skeleton*** includes the bones of your arms, hands, legs, feet, hips, and shoulder blades. Unlike the bones of the axial skeleton, bones of the appendicular skeleton move freely.

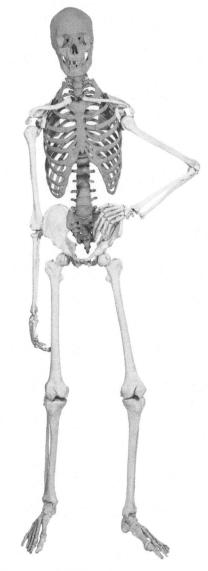

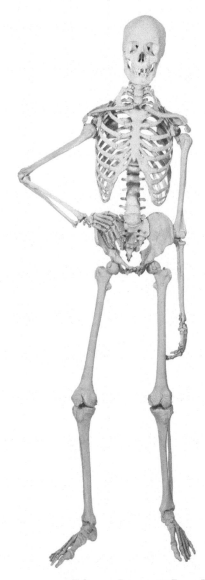

Axial Skeleton

Appendicular Skeleton

*Say it like this:
"ak-see-ull"

*Say it like this:
"app-un-**dik**-you-ler"

Turn back to the skeletons on the previous page. Look closely at the bones.

Do all of the bones look alike? Can you find some that are similar to each other in appearance? Let's see how bones are grouped according to what they have in common!

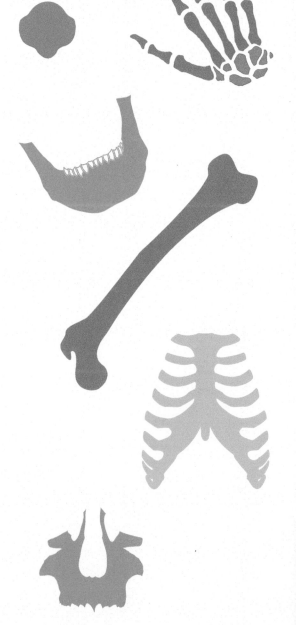

Long Bones

include the bones of your arms, legs, fingers, and toes. These bones are slightly curved, which helps them to absorb shock. Their strong shafts are made of compact bone. The inside of the wider ends have spongy bone that is covered with compact bone.

Arms • Legs • Fingers • Toes

Short Bones

are almost entirely made from spongy bone and sealed with a layer of compact bone. They are found in your wrists, ankles, and kneecaps.

Wrist Bones • Ankles • Kneecaps

Flat Bones

do not go up and down like long and short bones do. Your skull, ribs, sternum, hips, and shoulder blades are all flat bones. These flat plates of spongy bone are covered with compact bone.

Skull • Ribs • Sternum • Hips • Shoulder Blades

Irregular Bones

include facial bones such as the jawbone, the vertebrae that make up your spine, and the tiny bones (ossicles) in your ear.

Facial Bones • Spine • Ossicles in the Ear

Let's look at what makes up a long bone, shown here. Almost all bones include spongy bone, compact bone, and both red and yellow marrow.

Medullary* Cavity

runs down the middle of the long bone. In children, it's packed with red marrow. In adults, the medullary cavity becomes filled with fat (yellow marrow).

Nutrient Artery

runs the length of the medullary cavity. This artery is the main blood supply to the bone and helps it to stay healthy.

Compact Bone

is also known as cortical bone. Compact bone is the hard bony surface that you see when you look at skeletons. Compact bone is the heaviest type of bone and supports the weight of the body.

Spongy Bone

is also known as cancelous bone. It's really a network of many bony fibers that provide the bone with support. Spongy bone reminds us of a real sponge, with the sponge being the bony fibers and the air pockets being red or yellow marrow.

Red Marrow

is found within spongy bone and in the medullary cavity in children's bones. Both red and white blood cells are made in the red marrow.

*Say it like this: **"meh**-dull-lary"

Keeping it all Together!

Your bones need connective tissue like ligaments, tendons, and cartilage to help them move. These connective tissues join bone to bone and muscle to bone so you can move your body. Let's look at the diagram below to see the connective tissue inside your knee.

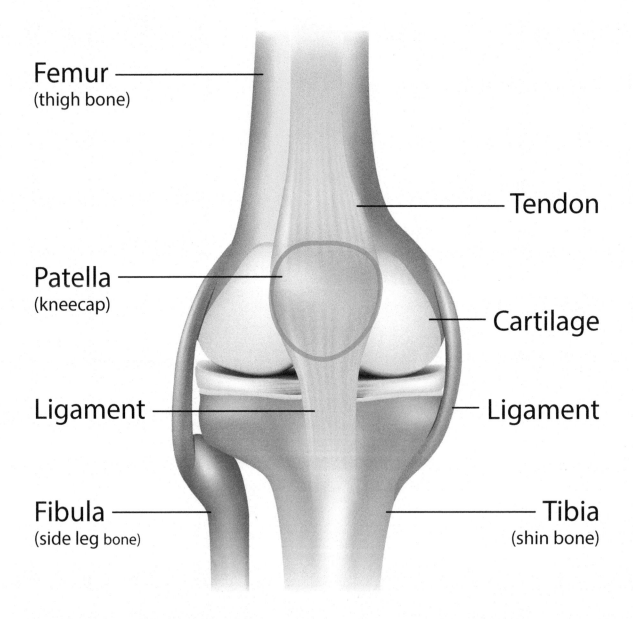

Femur — (thigh bone)

Tendon

Patella (kneecap)

Cartilage

Ligament

Ligament

Fibula (side leg bone)

Tibia (shin bone)

The smallest bone in your body is located in your middle ear. It's called the stapes.* Say it like this: "**STAY**-peas".

Cartilage

is stiff connective tissue that's not as hard as bone. Your nose and outer ear are made of cartilage. Cartilage is also between some bones, such as the meniscus between your femur and tibia.

Tendons

connect bone to muscle. Without ligaments and tendons, your bones couldn't move, regardless of how muscular you are!

Ligaments

connect bone to bone so they can work together. Locate the ligaments on the knee illustration. See how they are connecting bones?

BE A LABEL DETECTIVE!

Your bones need more than calcium to be strong. They need Vitamin D, too! Vitamin D helps your bones use calcium from foods like cheese, almonds, and yogurt. If you eat foods high in calcium and Vitamin D, plus add in bone-strengthening activities, you can build strong bones now and help prevent bone fractures when you're older.

Now, try out your detective skills!

Lots of foods have calcium, but Vitamin D is harder to find.

Take a look at the labels of foods that you eat. How many foods have Vitamin D? How many foods have calcium? Write their names in the appropriate areas.

VITAMIN D	CALCIUM

Know Your Skeletal System

Bones provide shape and support for our entire body, protect our organs, and allow us to move. What if we didn't have bones? Can you imagine Pinky standing on Bounski's shoulders while in disguise in 1922 St. Petersburg, in the middle of winter? They would be a squishy pile, like a melted snowman.

Both Calcium and Vitamin D are essential nutrients for bone health.

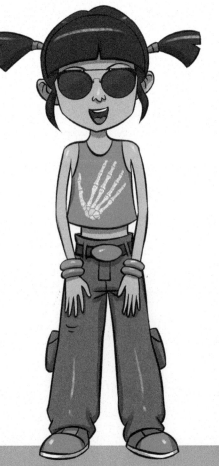

When the body receives calcium from food, it uses vitamin D to absorb that calcium into your small intestine. So vitamin D is as important as calcium.

Food can supply both these important nutrients, but your skin actually produces vitamin D when exposed to sunlight.

But what if you live someplace that does not have a lot of sunshine?

St. Petersburg, for example, is in a part of the world that gets very little sunlight compared to Cairo, Egypt or Yuma, Arizona. So if you live in northern Russia, you have to be sure to eat food rich in Vitamin D—especially during the winter!

On the other hand, your body cannot make its own calcium.

A need for calcium triggers
Bone Remodeling
the creation of new bone to replace old bone.

> Old bone?
> But I'm only a kid!
> How do I have old bone??

Bones of kids and adults of all ages are always renewing themselves. Another way bone remodeling is initiated is through exercise and other types of movement referred to as mechanical stress.

Running, **practicing ballet**, **lifting weights** — like Bounski carrying Pinky on his shoulders — are all examples of mechanical stress.

Know Your Skeletal System

Did you know you are "BONE to be wild"? Your bones are alive and are constantly reshaping themselves through the process of bone remodeling. You have bone cells called **osteoblasts*** and **osteoclasts***.

Osteoblasts work together as one team to build new bone. They receive instructions from certain proteins in the body, telling them it's time to make new bone.

Osteoclasts, on the other hand, eat up bone, making room for the osteo-blasts
to contribute new bone.

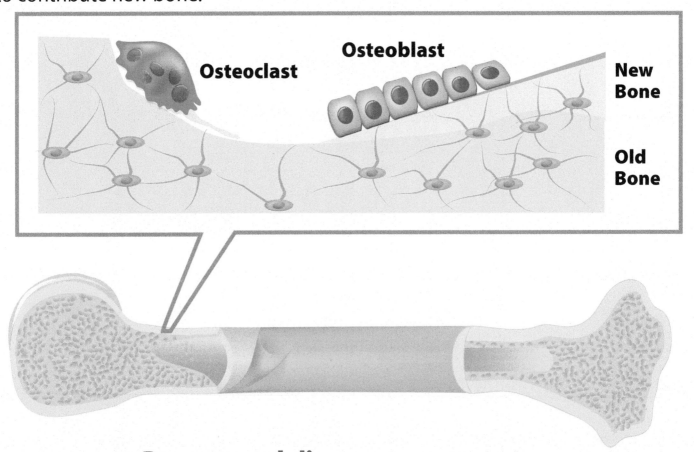

Bone remodeling serves many purposes,
including repairing minor damage caused by mechanical stress.

osteoblasts and osteoclasts

Say it like this: "**os**-tee-uh-blasts" and "**os**-tee-uh-clasts".

*Syllables in bold are the strongest.

Choosing not to expose your bones to stress may cause your bones to be thinner and to lose their shape and structure. Although "stress" is generally not something people want, when it means activity and exercise, the more physical, resistance-based activities you do, the heavier (or more dense) your bones will be.

This balancing act between remodeling and mechanical stress helps to keep your bones at an ideal size and weight given the amount of activity they endure.

Dr B.'s Note

More than **90% of the Calcium** in your body is stored in your **bones** and **teeth**.

Explore your BONES!

Here's a look at the entire skeleton.
Notice how each bone has a special name.
We often use common names like arm, finger,
or hips to describe bones. Did you know that
each bone has a scientific name, too?
The scientific names are used by doctors,
nurses, scientists, and now by you!

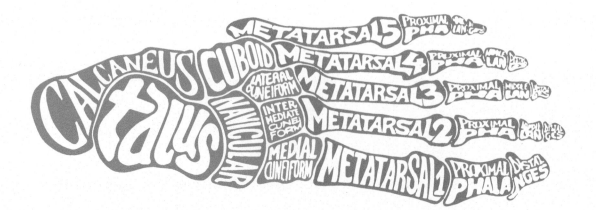

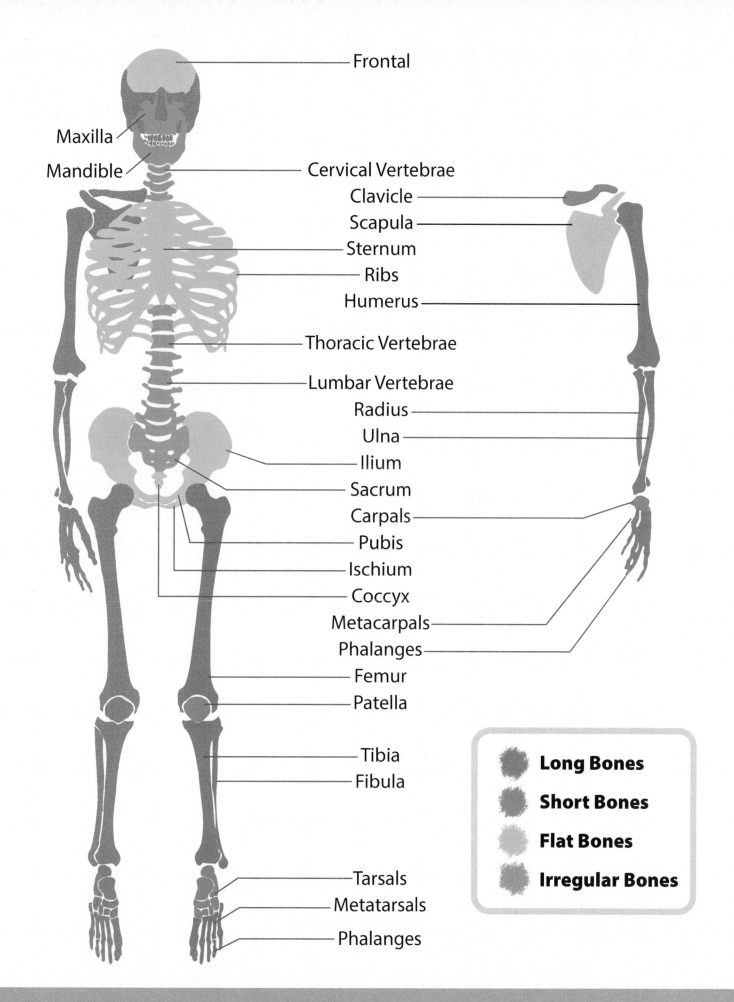

Frontal

Maxilla

Mandible

Cervical Vertebrae

Clavicle

Scapula

Sternum

Ribs

Humerus

Thoracic Vertebrae

Lumbar Vertebrae

Radius

Ulna

Ilium

Sacrum

Carpals

Pubis

Ischium

Coccyx

Metacarpals

Phalanges

Femur

Patella

Tibia

Fibula

Tarsals

Metatarsals

Phalanges

Long Bones

Short Bones

Flat Bones

Irregular Bones

A Bone to Pick

Sticks and Stones..? Let's Build Those Bones!

Get the Adventure 2 skeleton equipment (pages 52/53) and build your bones!

Materials:

- **Know Yourself skeleton**
- **Set of brads**
- **Hole puncher**
- **Optional: Colored pencils**

Directions:

PREPARING THE BONES

1. Punch out all of your skeleton parts.

2. Organize the bones by section, as shown here by color. (Optional: color each bone accordingly).

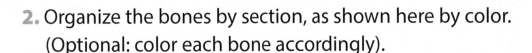

Yellow = upper extremities, shoulders, and collar

Orange = rib cage and spine

Purple = lower extremities and pubic bones

Green = head

3. Starting with the bones of **the upper extremities**, pick up a bone and compare it to the same one in your own body. Imagine how and where it connects. Now repeat this process for all the bones.

CONNECTING THE BONES

4. Use your hole puncher and brads to connect the bones to each other, section by section. For example, start by connecting the five bones of the left side of **the upper extremities** to each other and set aside. Since the body is symmetric, you can repeat these steps for the five bones on the right side.

5. Repeat step 4 for the **orange** and **purple** sections.
The **green** stands alone.

Note: Some of the Know Yourself skeleton bones are missing a punch hole showing where to insert a brad — you'll find them at the end of each radius, both clavicles, and the sacrum.

FORMING THE SKELETON

6. Connect **the head** to **the rib cage and spine** and secure with a brad.

7. Connect **the rib cage and spine** to the bones of **the upper extremities** (keeping the scapulas free to move behind the rib cage) and secure with a brad.

8. Connect **the pubis bone** to **the bones of the lower extremities**, then **the pubis** to **the spine** and secure with brads.

9. And finally, punch a hole in the top of the skeleton so you can hang it up!

A Bone to Pick

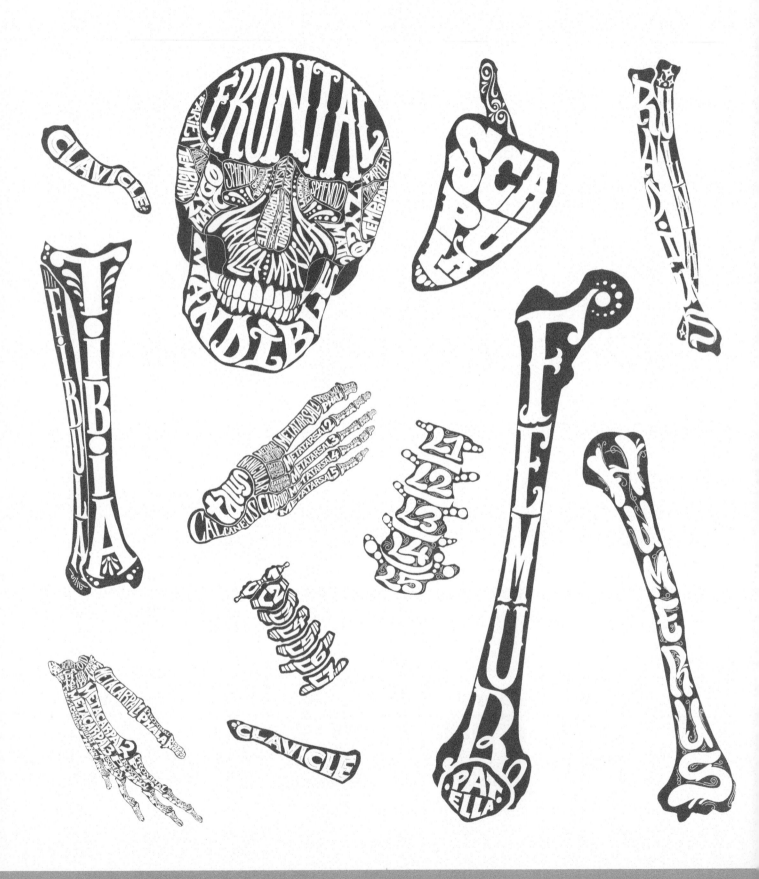

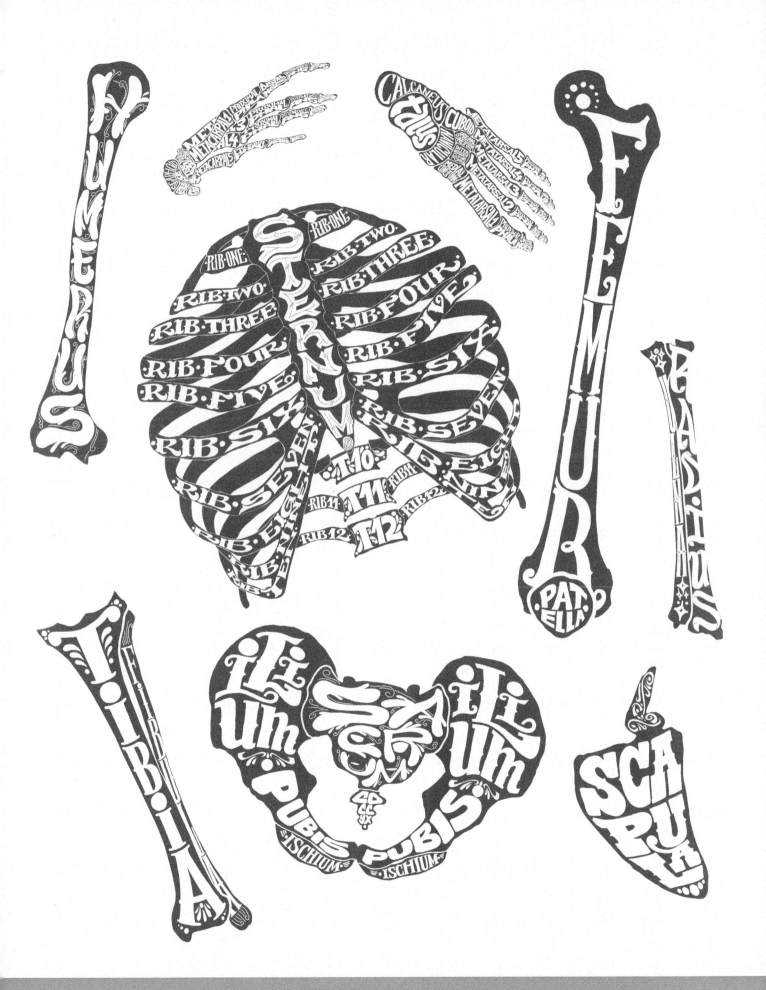

A Bony Twist!

Get ready for A Bony Twist on listening to some of your favorite music!

Materials:

- **White paper**
- **Markers**
- **Your completed skeleton from "A Bone to Pick"**
- **Music**

This is a fun game you can play with one other person or add more people for more fun. To play, you will need to first create some signs with bones names. Use the skeleton you built in the previous activity "**A Bone to Pick**" for reference.

Directions:

PREPARING YOUR BONE SIGNS

1. Take your paper and markers out onto a flat surface. Place your skeleton nearby or assistance.

2. To design your signs, you will need to write in large, uppercase writing that can be read from a distance. Write either a bone or group of bones onto each piece of paper. Reference your skeleton if you need help remembering the name of a bone or bone group.

3. Make as many or as few signs as you like!

4. Once your signs are complete, grab your favorite music, a friend, and get ready to twist!

HOW TO PLAY

1. Playing the game is easy. Just turn on your favorite jams and see how well you know your bones. When your friend shows you a sign, bust a bony move using whichever bones are shown on the signs you made.

Note: You can make **A Bony Twist** more challenging by writing the name of each bone on each piece of paper, or less challenging by just writing groups of bones on each piece of paper. For example, write femur, tibia, or scapula for a challenge. For something a bit easier, use groups of bones instead - for example, upper extremities, rib cage and spine, lower extremities, and head.

femur

tibia

Adventurer, how do you feel after dancing to your favorite song?

Do you feel emotionally happier or physically a little out of breath?

Checkin with yourself and take down some notes.

head   spine   radius

Mighty Bones

When your bones are stressed, your body works to repair them and make them thicker so they won't break! It might be confusing how just adding a bit more bone can make something stronger, so let's use a visual example of how just a little bit more material can make something unbreakable!

Materials:

- **A piece of paper you don't care about.** A good use of junk mail!

Directions:

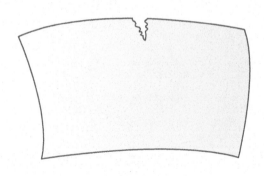

1. Try to rip the paper, just a little. It's easy, isn't it!

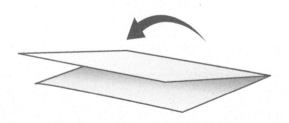

2. After you rip it, take the piece of paper and fold it in half. This is similar to what your body does, with osteoblasts layering on new bone to make it stronger.

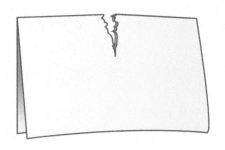

3. Now try to rip the paper!
You should still be able to do it,
but it will be a little bit more difficult.

4. Keep folding the paper
and trying to rip it.

- **Can you rip it with four folds?**

- **How about five??**

Know Yourself! Draw Yourself!

Take a moment to draw the skeleton in you! Use some chalk to draw yourself and later label your skeleton self. Use your **Bone to Pick** skeleton if you need help!

Materials:

- **Colored chalk**
- **A dry sidewalk**
- **A friend**
- **Bone to Pick skeleton**

Directions:

1. Once you find the perfect sidewalk location, ask a friend to outline your body using a piece of chalk.

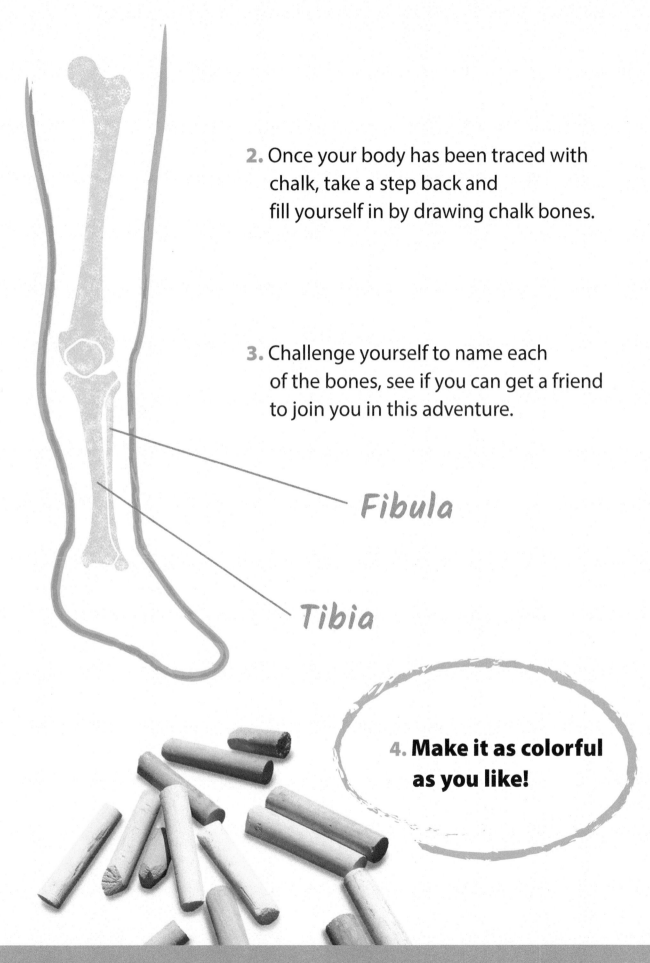

2. Once your body has been traced with chalk, take a step back and fill yourself in by drawing chalk bones.

3. Challenge yourself to name each of the bones, see if you can get a friend to join you in this adventure.

Fibula

Tibia

4. **Make it as colorful as you like!**

Building Bones

Have you ever pondered about what makes your skeleton so strong and able to interact with the world?

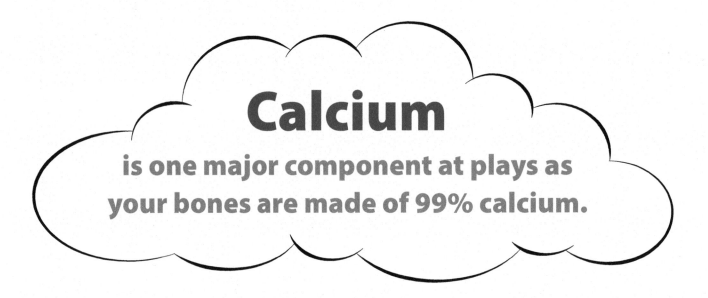

Calcium

is one major component at plays as your bones are made of 99% calcium.

Some sources of calcium can come from calcium-rich foods you eat like milks and cheeses, leafy green vegetables (think brussel sprouts, parsley, kale, broccoli, and bok choy).

One thing to note when thinking about building strong bones is that balance is key. A few other vital food nutrients for bone development are **vitamins C**, **D**, and **K**, **phosphorus**, **protein**, **magnesium**, **healthy fats**, and **sodium**.

Don't forget that doing daily **exercise**, **movement**, and **drinking enough water** are other important factors as well.

What foods can you add to your diet if you want to ensure you are getting a healthy supply of calcium and nutrients? Try taking down a few ideas for your next grocery trip!

Think on Your Feet!

Posture en Pointe

What's the point of keeping your posture on point? It's simple. Psychology follows physiology; your state of mind is naturally connected to the way your body functions. When you sit or stand up straight so you appear confident and alert, you actually promote feeling confident and alert. While your spine and muscles are the physical foundation of your posture, your posture supports and can even change your state of mind. Even better, this small but positive shift positively affects the way others perceive you.

When you feel shy, nervous, or unsure, remember you can change how you feel in an instant. Ask yourself, **"How would I carry myself if I were confident and calm?"** If you don't know, imagine a person you perceive as confident and try to do what they do: drop your shoulders, lift your chest, hold your head high. With awareness of your body and mind, you can transform doubt into daring, anxiety into ability—all while you're walking down the hall! How cool is that?

MINDFUL MOMENT

Has anyone ever told you to

"Stand tall", "Chin up", or "Keep your head up"?

These phrases are meant as words of encouragement and reassurance.
Thank someone who has said them to you,
or say them to someone else who needs them.

Ballet Basics for Posture & Alignment

Russia has produced some of the most famous ballet dancers of the modern era, including **Mikhail Baryshnikov**, **Anna Pavlova**, **Ekaterina Maximova**, and **Rudolf Nureyev**.

Ballet helps build muscle and bone. It can improve your posture and more!
Have you ever noticed how a ballet dancer walks, sits, or stands?
Balance and core strength help develop confidence both on stage and off.

Try these five ballet poses to build bone, body awareness, and your inner Baryshnikov.

Follow the explanations on the next pages.

First Position

Look down at your feet.
Are they positioned correctly?

How to do:

To begin, stand with your heels together and toes facing out to either side, in a comfortable V shape.

Make sure the bottoms of your feet are flat on the ground.

Your legs should be straight.

Make a big circle with your arms, like you're holding a beach ball, hands a bit in front of your belly button.

Second Position

The reason your toes face out is actually because you are rotating your whole leg. This rotation is called **turnout** and comes from your hip.

How to do:

Move your right foot, hip distance apart, toes pointing out.

Keeping your arms rounded, raise them out to either side.

Imagine a marble rolling very slowly down your humerus, along the radius, and falling off distal phalange #2.

Take a moment to notice how stable and strong you feel.

2

Third Position

Third position helps prepare dancers for fifth and is used more for strengthening than performance.

How to do:

Cross your right foot in front, both sets of toes pointing out, with your right heel touching the arch of your left foot.

Return your right arm to first position, holding an imaginary beach ball.

Your left arm is rounded and resting just above your belly button.

Try not to stick your butt out and imagine your two scapulas relaxing down.

3

Fourth Position

Somewhat challenging, fourth position is open and helps dancers get ready to pirouette or turn!

How to do:

From third position, slide your right foot forward, about one foot's distance.

Keep your toes pointed out, raise your left arm up, just above your frontal bone.

Can you adjust your weight so that it is evenly distributed over both feet?

Imagine your sternum long and the top of your skull reaching up to the sky.

Fifth Position

Fifth position is probably the most demanding. Be nice to your joints and don't force this position – instead, go back to third to engage your inner thighs and strengthen your hip rotation.

How to do:

Slide your right foot back toward your left.

Keeping your toes facing out, rest your right heel against the inside of your left toes.

Raise both your arms, rounded, with your imaginary beach ball. Can you keep your scapula from moving up toward your neck?

Don't forget to keep your butt from sticking out! That will help with stability.

5

POWER POSE

Have you ever noticed how superheroes stand?

Often heroes like Wonder Woman and Superman are pictured with feet wide, hands on hips, and chest up, ready to face the world! Even without X-ray vision, super-strength, or the ability to fly, you, too, can feel as bold and powerful as a crime-fighting marvel.

Studies on body language have proven that **standing in a POWER POSE for 3 minutes** changes your state of mind and builds immediate confidence. Try this in a mini exercise; write down how you feel before the power pose, stand in the power pose for 3 minutes and write down how you feel again. Anything change? What a great exercise to do in the bathroom before standing up in class to give a report or before auditioning for a part in a play.

Besides making you look heroic, this posture has other cool benefits:

- Allows your lungs room to expand, which aids respiration.

- Gives your brain (via the spinal cord) a clearer path to communicate with the rest of you, helping you move more efficiently.

- Promotes physical awareness and feeling comfortable in space, as well as with yourself.

Remember that posture connects to other things in your body: **gait** (how you walk), the state of your **nervous system**, and **joint health**.

The power of POWER POSE is that it's empowering in more ways than one!

Know Your Skeletal System

BONE

BONES

CALCIUM

MECHANICAL

MOVEMENT

OSTEOBLAST

OSTEOCLAST

REMODELING

STRESS

SUNLIGHT

TEETH

VITAMIN D

Answer keys on page 111.

```
M X C C O L M T J T V V M G O
A E D A I M H W S O I R U O J
H L C F L G K A S G T O K S J
S B D H I C L B M K A F K T V
S Q N L A C I T F Q M G N E L
R E N U O N R U A H I S D O N
X U U E S T I V M U N T X B I
S V T E C I G C N V D R T L E
J S N T E E T H A W N E Q A Z
O O B R A Q R C G L T S F S Z
B U V O K B J M O Z F S S T M
S V O F N P K N T R A H Q E K
R E M O D E L I N G U H G H A
F W S J R C D M O V E M E N T
Z O Q K V G E C V E M X L N G
```

Skele-ton of Information

Good work, adventurers!

Now that you know the skeletal system, let's review what you've learned!

Try to fill in the blanks.

Bones give us _ _ _ _ _ _ _ _ _ _ _/_ _ _ _ _ _ _ _ _ _ _ _,

protect our _ _ _ _ _ _ _ _ and let us _ _ _ _ _ .

The body gets _ _ _ _ _ _ _ _ from food and _ _ _ _ _ _ _ _ _ _ _

from food or sunlight and uses them together in the small intestine to help

you create bones.

Not having enough calcium or doing a lot of exercise can trigger a process

called _ _ _ _ _ _ _ _ _ _ _ _ _ _ _ _ _ .

There are two types of bone cells that work on a new bone,

_ _ _ _ _ _ _ _ _ _ _ _ _ which work to help your body produce new

bones, and _ _ _ _ _ _ _ _ _ _ _ _ _ which eat up old bone to make

room.

Stress is normally not a fun word, but when it comes to bones it's important

to prevent your bones from becoming __ __ __ __ __ __ __ __ and losing

their __ __ __ __ __ .

Some things that provide good stress for your bones are __ __ __ __ __ __ __ __ __

or __ __ __ __ __ __ __ __ __ . This stress helps your bones stay healthy!

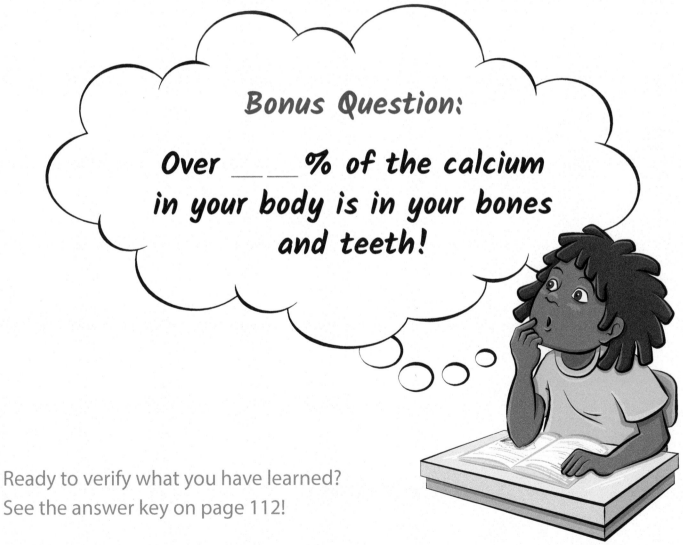

Bonus Question:

Over _____ % of the calcium
in your body is in your bones
and teeth!

Ready to verify what you have learned?
See the answer key on page 112!

Know Your Appetite

Experience Russian Foods

In 1920s Russia, most food choices were basic and minimal, but a cheerful ring-shaped breadstick called "**sushki**" was popular then — and still is today. Sushkis are like the bagel's younger cousin, but a drier version. In fact, "sushit" in Russian means drying out. Russian food shops sell sushkis on a string, like a necklace, and they are often referred to as a traditional tea bread.

In addition to the sushkis, you will find a **potato salad dish with dill**, representing hearty options for a Russian-inspired lunch with friends. Along with breads, Russian staples include meats, potatoes, and cabbage.

The body burns a lot of calories fighting the cold Russian winter, so high-calorie, high-starch foods are popular (as are thick winter coats!). It's not uncommon to find starchy and bread-focused foods combined with hearty ingredients in Russia's popular recipes.

Pancakes, **pirozhkis** (mini meat pies), and **honeycakes** are all examples of dishes prepared in Russian homes to both fill and warm the belly. Side dishes made with **cabbage**, **beets**, and **potatoes**, and garnishes such as **sour cream** and **herbs (usually dill)**, bring color and flavor to meals.

Pinky's Hint:

Read through the entire recipe before beginning to prepare food. This way, you'll know what equipment and ingredients are needed, and you'll be familiar with the steps involved.

 Whenever you see the chef's hat icon, it means **you'll need an adult's help**.

Приятного аппетита!*

(Prijatnovo Appetita)

That means **"Good Appetite!"** in Russian. You can say these words to wish someone a nice meal.

***Say it like this:**
Syllables in green are strongest.

"pre-yat-no-va — ah-pee-tee-tuh"

Recipes and food knowledge provided by Chef Polly Legendre of La Gourmande Catering.

Russian Potato Salad with Dill

Serves 4

Total time: 30 minutes

Ingredients:

- 1 lb small red potatoes
- 1/2 cup nonfat plain yogurt
- 1 teaspoon white vinegar
- 1/2 teaspoon salt
- 1/4 cup thinly sliced scallions
- 3 tablespoons chopped fresh dill
- pepper

Preparation:

1. Place the potatoes in a soup pot and cover with water. Turn on high heat and bring to a boil. Once the water boils, reduce the heat to medium and let simmer until the potatoes are tender. (Test the potatoes by carefully inserting a knife or fork into the center. If it goes in easily and the potatoes are tender, then they are done cooking).

2. Carefully pour the potatoes into a colander over a sink and let them cool.

3. In a small bowl, combine the yogurt, vinegar, salt, scallions, dill, and a little bit of pepper.

4. When the potatoes are cooled down enough to handle, cut them into quarters and place in a salad bowl.

5. Pour the yogurt mixture over the potatoes and gently stir until the potatoes are covered. **The salad is now ready to serve!**

 ## Show off your cooking skills!

Have your grown up take a photo, and share on social media using the hashtag:

#KnowYourAdventure

 KnowYourselfOAK   KnowYourselfOAK

Sushkis

Prep the dough

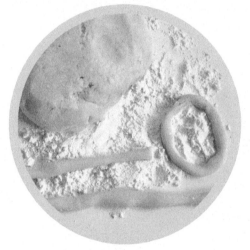

Roll it up

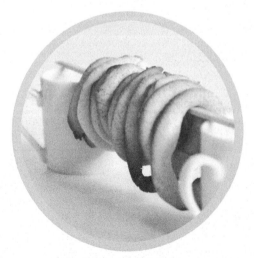

Bake and enjoy

Makes 60–75 individual sushkis

Prep time:
10 minutes

Bake time:
15-20 minutes

Note:

Baking time will depend on how thick/thin you made the sushki, your oven, and also how crunchy you prefer the sushki to be.

Ingredients:

- 1 can (14 oz) condensed milk
- 2 eggs
- 4 tablespoons softened butter
- 2 tablespoons sugar
- 1 teaspoon vanilla extract
- 1/2 teaspoon baking soda
- 1/4 teaspoon salt
- 4 cups flour
- Milk wash: 1/4 cup milk + 1 tsp sugar

Preparation:

1. Preheat the oven to 350 degrees.

2. Line a baking sheet with parchment paper.

3. In a large bowl, using a standing mixer with a paddle or whisk attachment, or using a hand mixer, mix the condensed milk, sugar, eggs, softened butter (the butter needs to be soft, or it won't incorporate into the batter), and vanilla.

4. In another bowl, whisk the flour, baking soda, and salt. (Switch to the dough hook attachment.) Add the flour gradually to the batter, and mix until combined.

   Note: If your eggs are on the smaller side, you might want to use only 3½ cups of flour. Also, the batter will be stiff, so if you don't have a mixer with a good engine, you might want to mix the last batch of flour in by hand.

5. Portion the dough into halves, then shape into two balls. Roll each ball of dough into a rope and pinch the ends together, making the rope as thick or thin as you like.

6. Place the shaped sushkis onto the prepared baking sheet, and brush them with the milk wash.

7. Bake in the preheated oven for 15 to 20 minutes.

8. Cool and store in a closed bag or an airtight container until you're ready to share and enjoy.

Like them on the crunchy side? Make them thin and bake longer. If you make them a little bit thicker, they will be softer.

Encourage friends and family to dunk them in tea or coffee or eat them plain.

Thoughts for Young Chefs

What is a Venn Diagram?

When you have to arrange a set of items, it's helpful to show what makes them similar and what makes them different. Named after its inventor, British mathematician John Venn, the Venn diagram is an organizational tool that does exactly this.

Made of overlapping circles, a **Venn diagram** represents the overall set within a boundary. The intersection of the circles indicates what characteristics two items have in common. The other sections show traits that the items do not share.

Mr. Venn wrote about Venn diagrams in his book, *Symbolic Logic*, which was published in 1881 and built upon other mathematicians' theories from as long ago as the early 1700s.

Look at the example below for the overall set, Living Creatures.

Take turns with a friend discussing each item and how it's organized in the example. Challenge each other to add two "items" to the "Set" not in the same section.

Living Creatures

Set = {spider, butterfly, human, pigeon, _____ , _____ }

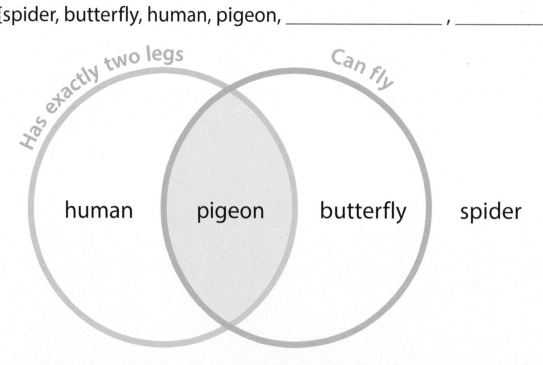

Next, try these Venn diagrams:

Types of Food

Set = {Russian potato salad, pizza, sushkis, French fries, _____ , _____ }

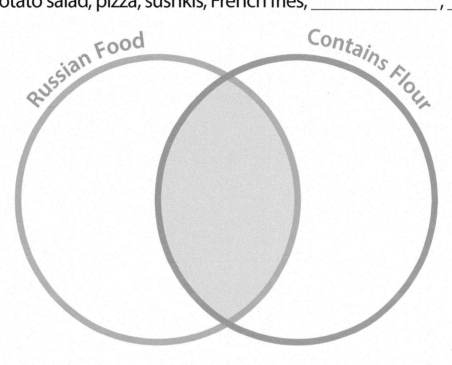

Parts of the Body

Set = {skull, eyeball, femur, stomach, _____ , _____ }

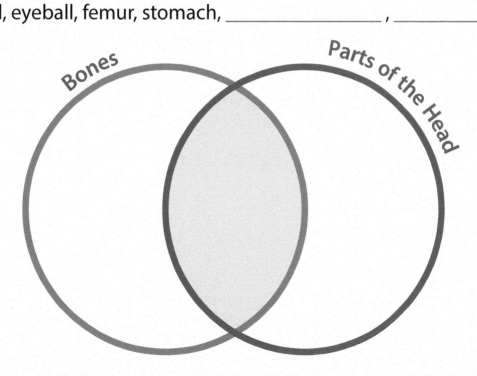

Rush-In And Bone Up

Adventure 2 Information Review

Hello Adventurers!

You have done fantastic work learning about your skeletal system and the history of Early 20th Century Russia. Right before this bone-tingling adventure ends and you take all of your twenty-seven hand bones to give yourself a nice, warm pat on the back, we have just a few last questions for you.
Write down what you think below!

What are some ways a skeletal system was able to help famous dancers in early 20th century Russia **perform spectacular ballets?**

_____

_____

_____

_____

_____

_____

_____

Can you think of which bones they needed to complete dances (use your skeleton for help)?

_____

_____

_____

_____

_____

_____

_____

_____

_____

_____

Rush-In And Bone Up
(continuation)

Next, try and describe an activity that you do for fun and name the bones that allow you to play.

_____

_____

_____

_____

_____

How do fun activities make you feel?

_____

_____

_____

_____

Russia is home to some of the most famous artwork and monuments in the world, **from The Imperial Palace to the Fabergé eggs. It also has many places where there is so little sunlight people need to worry about what food they eat in the winter to make sure they get Vitamin D.**

Art is something that often helps people feel better in places that are dark or difficult. **Why do you think that is?**

_____

_____

_____

_____

_____

What are some things that make you feel better in difficult times?

_____

_____

_____

_____

Further Reading

History for Kids

- Learn more about the life of **Peter Carl Fabergé**, the man who created and designed the **Fabergé eggs**. This was curated by the New World Encyclopedia, a project that has experts vet Wikipedia articles while retaining their links to sources.

  https://www.newworldencyclopedia.org/entry/Peter_Carl_Faberg%C3%A9

- Dive deeper into the causes of the **Russian Civil War** on Kiddle, a visual search engine designed to be safe for kids.

  https://kids.kiddle.co/Russian_Civil_War9

Nonfiction for Younger Readers

- Simon, Seymour.
  Bones: Our Skeletal System (**ages 7-10**)

Nonfiction for Older Readers

- Fleming, Candace.
  The Family Romanov: Murder, Rebellion, and the Fall of Imperial Russia (**age 12+**)

LOOPS CREW: PART 2
THE COUNCIL OF EIGHT

THE SKELETAL SYSTEM

The Circulatory System

KNOW YOURSELF

3

The Circulatory System

The Zen is mightier than the Sword

The year is 1553 and this time you land in Dengfeng County in China, the Henan Province. Your mentor is a warrior monk named Tianyaun and he is mighty. You may be surprised where his strength, courage, and calm are rooted. Explore the circulatory system of the body.

CHINA

The year is 1553 and this time you land in **Dengfeng County in China, the Henan Province.** Your mentor is a warrior monk named Tianyaun and he is mighty. You may be surprised where his strength, courage, and calm are rooted. Explore the circulatory system of the body.

Get to Know...

Dr. Bonyfide

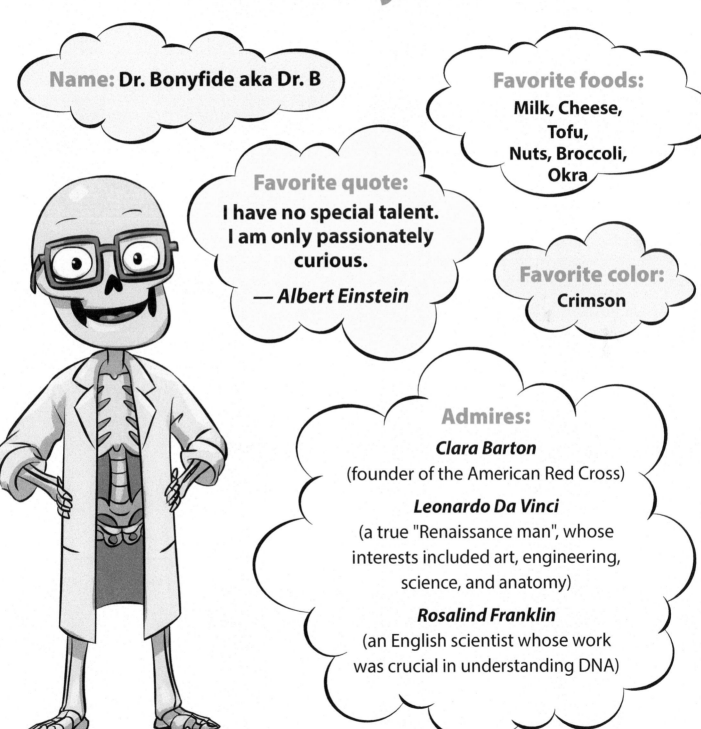

Name: Dr. Bonyfide aka Dr. B

Favorite foods:
Milk, Cheese,
Tofu,
Nuts, Broccoli,
Okra

Favorite quote:
I have no special talent.
I am only passionately
curious.
— *Albert Einstein*

Favorite color:
Crimson

Admires:

Clara Barton
(founder of the American Red Cross)

Leonardo Da Vinci
(a true "Renaissance man", whose
interests included art, engineering,
science, and anatomy)

Rosalind Franklin
(an English scientist whose work
was crucial in understanding DNA)

Answer Keys

All Tsar Knowledge

During the early 20th century, Alexander Maximov, a <u>h i s t o l o g i s t</u>

created the term "stem cell" and demonstrated that all blood cells develop from

a <u>p r e c u r s o r</u>. Alexander fled St. Petersburg in <u>1 9 2 2</u>,

traveling to the United States to teach <u>a n a t o m y</u>.

St. Petersburg is the most <u>n o r t h e r n</u> major city in the world.

Its many monuments contribute to the cultural importance that St. Petersburg

has to Russia. Monuments you may find visiting are The Mariinsky Opera

& Ballet Theater, The Imperial <u>P a l a c e</u>, and The Hermitage.

In the time before <u>V l a d i m i r   L e n i n</u> and the Bolsheviks had

overthrown the government and fought for Russia to be a <u>c o m m u n i s t</u>

country, the tsar ruled over the country with <u>a b s o l u t e</u> power.

The struggle to end private ownership and the Bolshevik party's rise to p o w e r was marked by violence. One famous treasure, created under tsar rule were the extravagant F a b e r g é eggs, first made as an E a s t e r gift.

After the death of Vladimir Lenin, Joseph S t a l i n led the Soviet U n i o n through both World War II and the Cold War. While World War II was known for being the most deadly war in history, no direct war ever took place during the C o l d W a r. The Cold War was a result of tension between the U n i t e d S t a t e s and the Soviet Union and their desires to be the strongest m i l i t a r y power in the world. S p a c e exploration was symbolic of power and s c i e n t i f i c achievement at that time.

Bonus: How many letters does the Russian language use?

3 3

Answer Keys

20th Century Russia Crossword

1 S
U
S
2 V H
4 B O L S H E V I K S **3** T
B A K S
O D I A
5 S I R
O **6** M A R I N S K Y
V M
I I
E R
7 S T P E T E R S **8** B U R G
L A
N L
9 M A X I M O V T
N I
10 C O L D

```
M X C C O L M T J T V V M G O
A E D A I M H W S O I R U O J
H L C F L G K A S G T O K S J
S B D H I C L B M K A F K T V
S Q N L A C I T F Q M G N E L
R E N U O N R U A H I S D O N
X U U E S T I V M U N T X B I
S V T E C I G C N V D R T L E
J S N T E E T H A W N E Q A Z
O O B R A Q R C G L T S F S Z
B U V O K B J M O Z F S S T M
S V O F N P K N T R A H Q E K
R E M O D E L I N G U H G H A
F W S J R C D M O V E M E N T
Z O Q K V G E C V E M X L N G
```

Skele-ton of Information

Bones give us <u>s h a p e   a n d</u>/<u>o r   s u p p o r t</u>, protect our <u>o r g a n s</u> and let us <u>m o v e</u>.

The body gets <u>c a l c i u m</u> from food and <u>V i t a m i n   D</u> from food or sunlight and uses them together in the small intestine to help you create bones.

Not having enough calcium or doing a lot of exercise can trigger a process called <u>b o n e   r e m o d e l i n g</u>.

There are two types of bone cells that work on a new bone, <u>o s t e o b l a s t s</u> which work to help your body produce new bones, and <u>o s t e o c l a s t s</u> which eat up old bone to make room.

Stress is normally not a fun word, but when it comes to bones it's important to prevent your bones from becoming t h i n n e r and losing their s h a p e.

Some things that provide good stress for your bones are e x e r c i s e or a c t i v i t y. This stress helps your bones stay healthy!

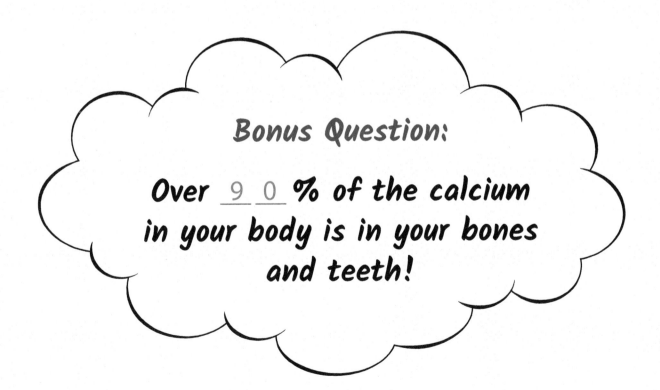

Bonus Question:

Over 9 0 % of the calcium in your body is in your bones and teeth!

CREATED WITH LOVE
BY THE
KNOW YOURSELF TEAM